MW00827700

Ava & Mae
Own a Lemonade Stand

WRITTEN BY
Brittney Dias

ILLUSTRATED BY
Iman Purnell

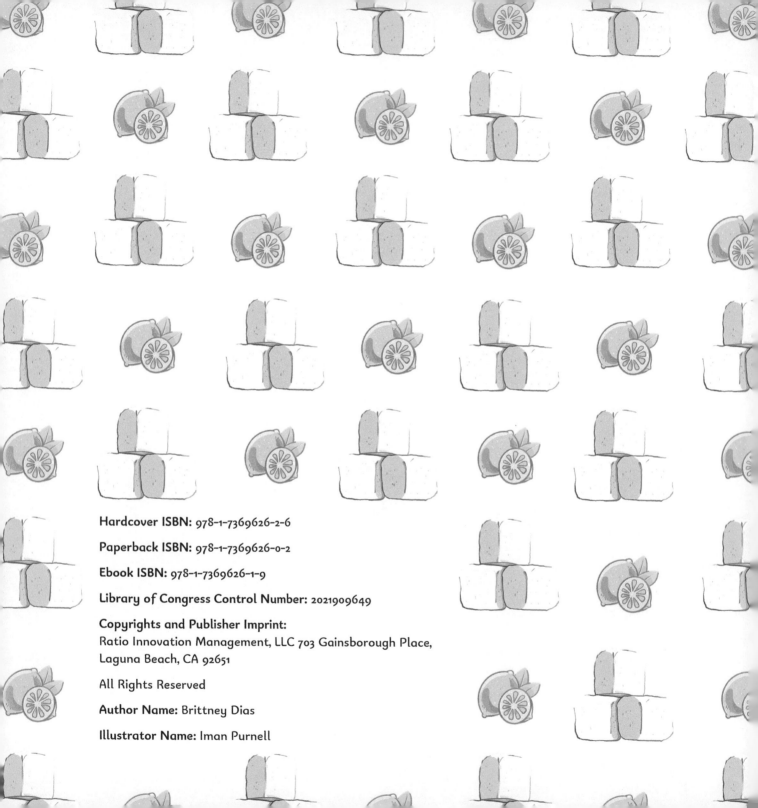

Hardcover ISBN: 978-1-7369626-2-6

Paperback ISBN: 978-1-7369626-0-2

Ebook ISBN: 978-1-7369626-1-9

Library of Congress Control Number: 2021909649

Copyrights and Publisher Imprint:
Ratio Innovation Management, LLC 703 Gainsborough Place,
Laguna Beach, CA 92651

All Rights Reserved

Author Name: Brittney Dias

Illustrator Name: Iman Purnell

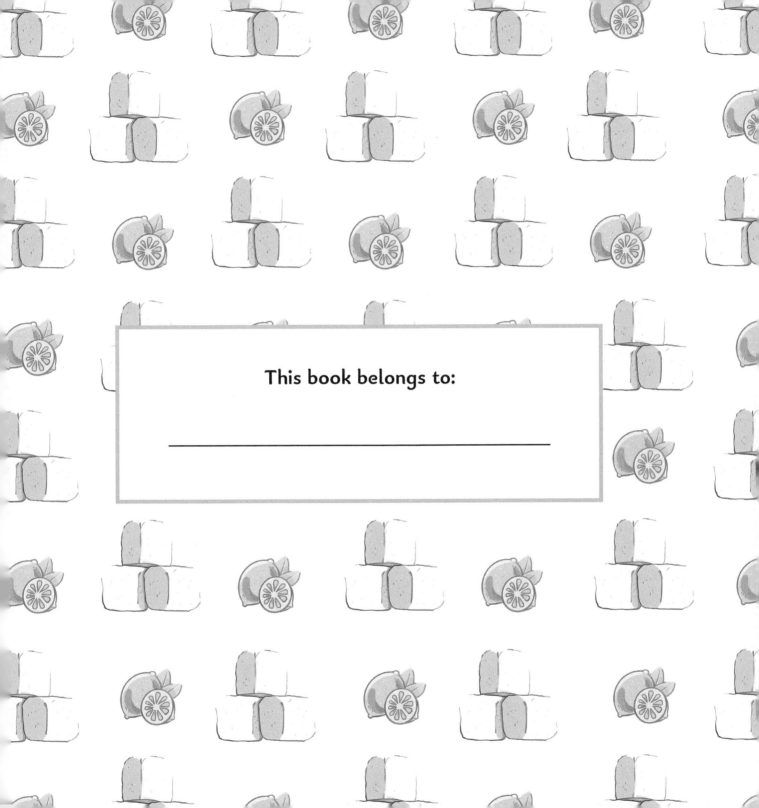

This book belongs to:

_____

This is Ava and her sister Mae.

Today is their first time at the Summer Start Fair!

They win a bright yellow ball and a big blue teddy bear. They even stop to buy some yummy pretzels.

They have five dollars left to get drinks.

The fair is so busy that the drinks are all sold out!

What should they do?

Mae has an idea . . .

"Let's go home and have some homemade lemonade!"

Mae loves creating and working with her hands.

No matter the time, no matter the day,
Ava and Mae find a way!

There's always lemonade
at Ava and Mae's home.

The lemonade is made
with juicy lemons from
their tall lemon tree.

The special lemons
make their lemonade
extra tasty.

"What about everyone else at the fair?" asks Ava. "What will they have to drink?"

Ava has an idea . . .

"We can sell lemonade at the fair so no one will be thirsty!" Ava loves to make big plans. "What a great idea!" says Mae.

"Let's go step by step," Ava says as she grabs a pencil and paper.

The first step is to gather supplies and store them in their big red wagon.

A spoon to stir
A knife to cut

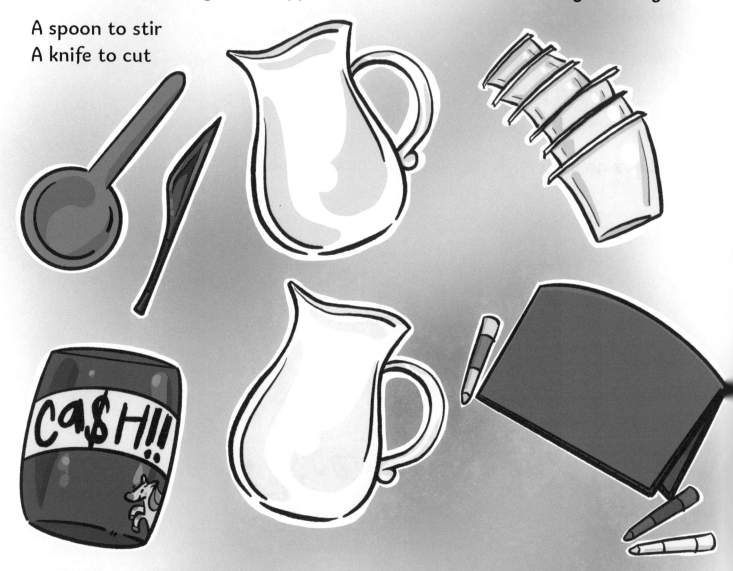

Two pitchers and lots of cups
A cash jar to hold their revenue
And a poster board and markers to make a business sign.

No matter the time, no matter the day, Ava and Mae find a way!

The second step is to gather more lemons.

They go to their backyard to get lemons from the tree.
It stands so big and tall above the ground.

How will they ever reach them?

They look for a ladder, but there's no ladder in their shed! What will they do?

"I've got an idea!" says Ava.

"Here!" she says. "Get on my shoulders!"

Ava kneels down below the tree.

Mae's eyes are wide as she stares up at the tree . . .

Will she ever reach the lemons?

Mae builds up the courage to climb on Ava's shoulders.

Her legs are short and shaky, but she doesn't give up.

Mae reaches and reaches, and finally picks a lemon right before both girls wobble and fall.

Mae gets back up. She picks lemons until the bag is finally full!

No matter the time, no matter the day, Ava and Mae find a way!

The third step is to gather the rest of the ingredients.

Now that Ava and Mae have the lemons,
Ava places a water jug in their wagon.

They look in the cabinet for sugar . . .

Just imagine if they sold lemonade with no sugar!
Then Mae has an idea . . .

"We can go to Betty's bakery! She's sure to have some sugar!" says Mae.

"What a great idea!" Ava says.

The girls place a thermos of lemonade in their wagon and run to the bakery as fast as they can.

Ava and Mae run into the bakery.

The smell of sweet cookies and pie fill their noses.

"Hi girls!" Ms. Betty says with a big smile. "What can I help you with today?"

"We need some sugar for our lemonade stand!" says Ava. "Do you have any extra?"

"Girls, I've got a business to run," says Ms. Betty. "I can't afford to give sugar away willy nilly!"

"Please, Ms. Betty? This is the best lemonade around. We'll even trade some of our special lemons," says Ava.

"I already have enough lemons!" Ms. Betty frowns.

How will the girls get their sugar? Suddenly, Mae has an idea.

She pours lemonade from the thermos into a cup.

"Here, Ms. Betty. Try a **sample**."

Betty the baker takes a sip of their lemonade and her face lights up.

"Wow!" says Ms. Betty. "This is the best lemonade I've ever tasted. Your lemons rcally are special."

"I'll tell you what. I'll give you this sugar in exchange for three of your juicy lemons. They'll taste great in the lemon pie I'm making today!"

"Deal!" say Ava and Mae. They make a **business deal** and trade some of their lemons for Ms. Betty's sugar.

No matter the time, no matter the day, Ava and Mae find a way!

The fourth step is to find a table.

They need somewhere to make and sell their lemonade. "Where will we find a table?" Mae asks Ava.

As they think of what to do, Ava sees a yard sale sign. "Maybe we can find a table over there!" she says. They walk up to the yard sale.

Guess what they see?

A bright yellow table!

It's the perfect table for their business, but it's ten dollars. All they have is five dollars left from the fair.

Oh no! What will they do?

They find the owner of the yard sale.

"Hi!" says Ava. "We're opening a lemonade stand for the Summer Start Fair. We love your table, but we only have five dollars!"

"Sorry, no discounts," says the owner. "Ten dollars is ten dollars."

"Here!" says Mae, with a determined smile.
She hands the owner a small cup of lemonade.
"Once you try THIS lemonade, you'll want a
thermos to yourself!"

"Wow!" he says as he licks his lips. "This lemonade is so good!"

He pauses for a second.

"I can tell this lemonade will be a hit. I'll sell you this table for five dollars now if you agree to pay the rest back once you've earned a **profit** from your lemonade stand."

"Deal!" say Ava and Mae.

They used **negotiations** to get their table!

"Good job!" says Mae as she gives Ava a high five.

"It was a smart idea to **invest** our money in a table for our lemonade stand!" says Ava.

Now the girls are finally on their way back to the fair.

No matter the time, no matter the day, Ava and Mae find a way!

Ava and Mae hurry back to the fair.

They set up their table and make two pitchers of their tasty lemonade. They pour some into cups and set up their cash jar.

They are ready for business!

The only thing missing are the **customers**!

The girls think and think, but they can't figure out what to do. How can they get people to buy their tasty lemonade?

"I know!" says Mae. "We forgot to make our sign!"

Ava and Mae remember that their last step is to advertise.

Since Mae loves to create things, she draws a colorful sign. They place it on their table for everyone to see.

"COME GET YOUR FRESH SQUEEZED LEMONADE!" yell Ava and Mae. After a few minutes, the fairgoers gather one by one to get a cup of the tastiest lemonade around!

Ava and Mae are the youngest **business owners** at the fair.

Ava and Mae went step by step to open their very own business.

They made **negotiations**, **investments**, **advertisements**, and more to make their dreams come true.

Things weren't always easy, but their hard work and great ideas finally paid off.

No matter the time, no matter the day, Ava and Mae find a way!

Advertisement
A message or announcement that promotes a good or service.

Business deal
An agreement between two or more businesses where there is usually an exchange of goods between businesses.

Business Owners
People who own, operate, and make decisions for a business.

Customers
Someone who buys a product or service.

Investment
The act of spending money on a business in order to gain profit in the future.

Negotiations
A discussion that helps reach a compromise that benefits each person.

Profit
The money a business earns once its revenue is higher than its investments.

Revenue
The money that flows into a business from its customers.

Sample
A small portion of a product that potential customers can try for free to see if they like the product.